ENVIRONMENTAL ASSESSMENT

A GUIDE TO THE PROCEDURES

LONDON: HMSO
DEPARTMENT OF THE ENVIRONMENT
WELSH OFFICE

CONTENTS

i

APPENDICES

Environmental assessment is an important technique for ensuring that the likely effects of new development on the environment are fully understood and taken into account before the development is allowed to go ahead. This booklet, which is intended primarily for developers and their advisers, explains how requirements for the environmental assessment of major projects (on which there is relevant European Community (EC) law) have been incorporated into consent procedures in the UK.

The EC Directive on 'The assessment of the effects of certain public and private projects on the environment' (85/337/EEC) was adopted on 27 June 1985, and came into effect in July 1988. The full text of the Directive is reproduced at Appendix 7 to this booklet. The effect of the Directive is to require environmental assessment to be carried out, before development consent is granted, for certain types of major project which are judged likely to have significant environmental effects.

Parts I and II of this booklet explain the procedures which apply to projects which fall within the scope of the Directive and require planning permission in England and Wales. For such projects the Directive was given legal effect through the Town and Country Planning (Assessment of Environmental Effects) Regulations 1988 (SI No. 1199) which came into force on 15 July 1988 and apply to relevant planning applications lodged on or after that date. The full text of the Regulations is published separately by HMSO. For ease of reference, those parts of the Regulations which list the types of project to which they apply, and specify what information an environmental statement must contain, are reproduced at Appendices 1 and 3 to this booklet.

Formal guidance on the new procedures, directed principally at local planning authorities, was issued in DOE Circular 15/88 (Welsh Office Circular 23/88). Though the present booklet is meant to be reasonably self-contained, developers may need to refer to that circular, particularly for fuller information on how planning authorities are expected to judge the significance of a project's likely effects for the purpose of deciding whether environmental assessment is required.

Parts I and II also give some general guidance on the nature of environmental assessment, and on the practical aspects of preparing an environmental statement, which is applicable to all types of project.

Part III gives a brief account of the procedures which apply to other projects within the scope of the Directive which fall to be approved under procedures other than planning procedures, for example, motorways, harbour works and long distance pipelines. It also deals briefly with environmental assessment procedures in Scotland and Northern Ireland. For the detailed

1

requirements, reference will need to be made to the relevant statutory instruments and associated guidance (see Appendix 8 to this booklet).

Throughout this booklet, **environmental assessment** (EA) is used of the whole process whereby information about the environmental effects of a project is collected, assessed and taken into account in reaching a decision on whether the project should go ahead or not. (The expression 'environmental impact assessment' (EIA) is also in common use and for practical purposes is synonymous with EA.) An **environmental statement** is a document setting out the developer's own assessment of his project's likely environmental effects, which he prepares and submits in conjunction with his application for consent.

PART I

ENVIRONMENTAL ASSESSMENT (EA) AND PROJECTS WHICH REQUIRE PLANNING
PERMISSION

What is environmental assessment?

1 The term 'environmental assessment' describes a technique and a process
by which information about the environmental effects of a project is
collected, both by the developer and from other sources, and taken into
account by the planning authority in forming their judgement on whether the
development should go ahead. Authorities already obtain from developers
such information as they consider necessary to determine a planning
application, including information about environmental effects; and those
effects are among the material considerations which a planning authority
must already take into account when considering a planning application.
What is new about EA is the emphasis on systematic analysis, using the best
practicable techniques and best available sources of information, and on the
presentation of information in a form which provides a focus for public
scrutiny of the project and enables the importance of the predicted effects,
and the scope for modifying or mitigating them, to be properly evaluated by
the planning authority before a decision is given.

2 Properly carried out, EA will help **all** those involved in the planning
process. From the **developer's** point of view, the preparation of an
environmental statement in parallel with project design provides a useful
framework within which environmental considerations and design
development can interact. Environmental analysis may indicate ways in
which the project can be modified to anticipate possible adverse effects, for
example, through the identification of a better practicable environmental
option, or by considering alternative processes. To the extent that this is
done, the formal planning approval stages are likely to be smoother.

3 The requirement to prepare an environmental statement may at first sight
seem an unwelcome complication of already complicated planning
procedures. But in many cases what the Regulations do in practice is to bring
forward, to an earlier stage in the development of a project, work which
would in any case have to be undertaken at a later stage. This is particularly
true of major projects where the developer would in any case be expected to
provide full and detailed information about environmental effects. For other
projects, the preparation of an environmental statement may involve some
additional work. The Government believe that this is justified in the interests
of protecting the environment, so long as environmental assessment is
applied only to those projects which are of sufficient significance to call for it.

4 For the **planning authority** and other public bodies with environmental responsibilities, environmental assessment should provide a basis for better decision-making. To the extent that the implications of a new project are more thoroughly analysed before a planning application is made, and more comprehensive information is provided with the application, swifter decisions may also be possible. While the responsibility for compiling the environmental statement rests with the developer, he is expected to consult those with relevant information, and the Regulations specifically require that public authorities who have information in their possession which is relevant to the preparation of the environmental statement should make it available to the developer. This should ensure that the developer can obtain information from public bodies at an earlier stage than has generally been the case under normal planning procedures.

5 The **general public's** interest in a major project is often expressed as concern about the possibility of unknown or unforeseen effects. By providing a full analysis of a project's effects, an environmental statement can help to allay fears created by lack of information. At the same time it can help to inform the public on the substantive issues which the local planning authority will have to consider in reaching a decision. It is a requirement of the Regulations that the environmental statement must include a description of the project and its likely effects together with a summary in non-technical language. One of the aims of a good environmental statement should be to enable readers to understand for themselves how its conclusions have been reached, and to form their own judgements on the significance of the environmental issues raised by the project.

6 Environmental assessment can therefore be helpful to all those concerned with major projects. The following paragraphs describe the procedures for deciding whether EA is necessary in a particular case and, where it is, for carrying out the assessment. The procedure is intended to make the most of the potential benefits of EA, while keeping the process as simple and flexible as possible, and avoiding any duplication of existing planning procedures.

When is environmental assessment needed?

7 The Regulations apply to two separate lists of projects:

i 'Schedule 1 projects', for which EA is required in every case;

ii 'Schedule 2 projects', for which EA is required only if the particular project in question is judged likely to give rise to significant environmental effects.

Both lists are given in full in Appendix 1 to this booklet.

8 For Schedule 1 projects, whether or not a particular project falls within the scope of the Regulations will normally be clear: several of the definitions of Schedule 1 projects incorporate an indication of scale, in the form of a quantified threshold, which clearly identifies the projects requiring EA. Where there is any doubt about a project's inclusion in Schedule 1, the procedures described in paragraphs 12-17 below can be used to obtain an opinion from the planning authority or a direction from the Secretary of State.

9 For the much longer list of Schedule 2 projects, the issue turns on the likelihood of '**significant** environmental effects'.

How 'significance' will be assessed

10 For obvious reasons there can be no general definition of what constitutes significance in this context. General guidance on how to assess 'significance' is contained in DOE Circular 15/88 (Welsh Office Circular 23/88); and rulings may be obtained from the local planning authority or the Secretary of State on whether EA is required in particular cases. Essentially the circular suggests that there are 3 main criteria of significance:

i whether the project is of more than local importance, principally in terms of physical scale;

ii whether the project is intended for a particularly sensitive location, for example, a national park or a site of special scientific interest (SSSI), and for that reason may have significant effects on the area's environment even though the project is not on a major scale;

iii whether the project is thought likely to give rise to particularly complex or adverse effects, for example, in terms of the discharge of pollutants.

These are very general guidelines and, to assist in their application to particular cases, the circular also sets out a number of quantified thresholds and indicative criteria by reference to particular categories of development listed in Schedule 2 to the Regulations. These are reproduced in Appendix 2 to this booklet.

11 It will be obvious that none of these guidelines can be applied as hard and fast rules: circumstances are bound to vary greatly from case to case. Some large scale projects which exceed the specified thresholds may not be significant enough to require EA; some smaller projects, particularly in sensitive locations, may be candidates for EA. On the other hand, there is no general presumption that all Schedule 2 projects in sensitive locations will

require EA: for some such projects normal planning procedures will suffice. Nevertheless, the guidance in the circular should provide a starting point for consideration by the developer and the planning authority of the need for EA. If the matter is referred to the Secretary of State, he also will have regard to the published criteria.

Obtaining a ruling on the need for EA

12 A developer can decide for himself that his project falls within the scope of the Regulations so that an environmental statement will be needed. But the Regulations also provide a procedure which enables a developer to apply to the planning authority for an opinion on whether EA is needed in a particular case as soon as he can provide a basic minimum of information about the proposal. This must include a plan on which the site of the proposed development is identified, and a brief description of its nature and purpose and of its possible effects on the environment. The developer can of course supplement this with other information if he wishes.

13 Where such information can be provided, the developer may approach the planning authority at any time for an opinion on the need for EA. He can do this well in advance of any formal planning application, though any approach to the planning authority before the planning application stage is entirely voluntary. Where such an approach is made, the planning authority must give their opinion within 3 weeks, unless the developer agrees to a longer period. The planning authority may request further information from the developer, but this in itself does not extend the 3 week time limit, unless the developer agrees.

14 Where the planning authority express the opinion that a particular proposal requires EA, they must provide a written statement giving clear and precise reasons for their opinion. Both that statement and the developer's application for an opinion are then made available for public inspection at the same place as the Planning Register.

15 A developer who is dissatisfied with the planning authority's opinion that EA is required may refer the matter to the Secretary of State. The developer is simply required to copy the relevant papers to the DOE regional office (or in Wales the Welsh Office) and add whatever representations he wishes to make in the light of the planning authority's statement. The Secretary of State will then normally give his direction within 3 weeks of the developer's application; and, if his direction is to the effect that EA is required, it will be accompanied by a statement of reasons.

16 The broad intention of this procedure is to ensure that developers can obtain a clear ruling on the need for EA well before they reach the stage of lodging a formal planning application. This should minimise the possibility of delay or uncertainty at that stage. Where the matter is not raised until a formal planning application is lodged, the developer risks serious delay if either the planning authority or the Secretary of State rule that an environmental statement must be prepared. No action will be taken on the planning application until the developer has prepared his environmental statement and submitted it to the planning authority.

17 In most cases this procedure will give developers a firm decision on the need for EA as soon as they can provide basic information about their project. There may occasionally be cases where information which reaches the Secretary of State directly leads him to issue a direction when there has been no request for one from the developer; or to overrule a planning authority's opinion that EA is not required; or even, very exceptionally, to reverse an earlier direction of his own. This could, for instance, happen where a development proposal came to the Secretary of State's notice on 'call-in'; or where third party representations drew attention to aspects of a proposed development which were not known to the Secretary of State when his initial direction was given. Exceptionally, also, a planning authority who have given a pre-application opinion that EA is not required might consider it necessary to reverse that decision when the planning application is formally submitted. In that case the developer could, of course, apply to the Secretary of State for a direction.

Simplified planning zones and enterprise zones

18 Special considerations apply to projects proposed for simplified planning zones (SPZs) and enterprise zones (EZs).

Simplified planning zones

All Schedule 1 projects are excluded from the scope of SPZs and therefore require EA as part of the application for planning permission. Where the terms of SPZ schemes would permit Schedule 2 projects to be undertaken without specific planning permission, developers must notify the planning authority where they intend to undertake such development. This notification will give the planning authority and, where appropriate, the Secretary of State the opportunity to consider whether the project is likely to give rise to significant environmental effects. If so, planning permission will be required in the normal way and an environmental statement will need to be prepared. If not, the project will enjoy the benefit of the general permission granted by the SPZ scheme, and no separate application for planning permission will be necessary.

Enterprise zones

EZs which were designated before July 1988 are not affected by the provisions for EA. In the case of EZs designated after July 1988, if the planning scheme allows for Schedule 1 projects, EA must be carried out. As regards Schedule 2 projects, the same procedures apply as those for SPZs described above.

The arrangements in SPZs and EZs are explained in DOE Circular 24/88 (Welsh Office Circular 48/88).

PART II

19 The developer is responsible for preparing the environmental statement he must submit with his planning application. He may choose to engage consultants for some or all of the work. The preparation of the statement should be a collaborative exercise involving discussions with the local planning authority, statutory consultees and possibly other bodies as well. There is no prescribed form of statement, provided that the requirements of the Regulations are met.

20 The aim should be to provide as systematic and objective an account as is possible of the significant environmental effects to which the project is likely to give rise. Where the statement embodies or summarises the conclusions of more detailed work, sufficient information should be provided to enable those who wish to do so to verify the statement's conclusions and to identify the source of the information provided. The environmental statement must contain a non-technical summary which will enable non-experts to understand its findings.

Preliminary consultations

21 One of the main emphases of the process of environmental assessment is on the need for full and early consultation by the developer with bodies which have an interest in the likely environmental effects of the development proposal. If important issues are not considered at a very early stage, they may well emerge when a project's design is well advanced, and necessitate rethinking and delay. Ideally, EA should start at the stage of site selection and (where relevant) process selection, so that the environmental merits of practicable alternatives can be properly considered.

22 While a developer is under no formal obligation to consult about his proposal before the submission of a formal planning application, there are good practical reasons for doing so. Authorities will often possess useful local and specialised information which is relevant to a project's design, and officers may be able to give preliminary advice about local problems and about those aspects of the proposal that are likely to be of particular concern to the authority.

23 The timing of such informal consultations is at the developer's discretion; but it will generally be advantageous for them to take place as soon as the developer is in a position to provide sufficient information about his proposal

to form a basis for discussion. The developer can ask that any information provided by him at this preliminary stage should be treated in confidence by the planning authority and any other consultees. If, however, he seeks a formal opinion from the planning authority on the need for environmental assessment (see paragraphs 12-17 above) the information about the project which accompanies that request will be made public by the authority.

The content of the environmental statement

24 Developers and authorities should discuss the **scope** of an environmental statement before its preparation is begun. The formal requirements as to the content of environmental statements are set out in Schedule 3 to the Regulations, which is reproduced in Appendix 3 to this booklet. As a practical guide to the range of issues which may need to be considered, developers may find it helpful to use the checklist at Appendix 4 to this booklet as a basis for their discussions with the planning authority. The checklist is not meant to be regarded as a prescribed framework for all environmental statements. Its main purpose is to act as a guide or agenda for the preliminary discussions about the scope of the statement. By working through the checklist, the developer and the planning authority should be able to agree which features of the project will need most attention in the statement.

25 The comprehensive nature of the checklist at Appendix 4 should not be taken to imply that all environmental statements should cover every conceivable aspect of a project's potential environmental effects at the same level of detail. Whilst every environmental statement should provide a full factual description of the project, the emphasis of Schedule 3 is on the 'main' or 'significant' effects to which a project is likely to give rise. In many cases, only a few of the aspects set out in the checklist will be significant in this sense and will need to be discussed in the statement in any great depth. Other issues may be of little or no significance for the particular project in question, and will need only very brief treatment, to indicate that their possible relevance has been considered.

26 Although the planning authority may express views about the information that should be included in an environmental statement, the developer is responsible for the content of the statement he finally submits. However, developers should bear in mind that planning authorities have powers to call for additional information when considering environmental statements and planning applications, and that they are likely to use those powers if they consider that aspects of a submitted environmental statement are inadequate (see paragraph 39 below). There is no provision for any disagreement between the developer and the planning authority over the content of an

environmental statement to be referred to the Secretary of State, except through normal planning appeal procedures (see paragraph 43 below).

Statutory and other consultees; the general public

27 The Regulations give a particular role in environmental assessment to those public bodies with statutory environmental responsibilities who must be consulted by the planning authority before a Schedule 1 or a Schedule 2 planning application is determined. A full list of these 'statutory consultees' is given in Appendix 5 to this booklet.

28 Where the planning authority (or the Secretary of State) rule that EA is required, those bodies which are statutory consultees for the particular project in question will be notified and the developer will be informed accordingly. The effect of this notification is to put those bodies under an obligation to provide the developer (on request) with any information in their possession which is likely to be relevant to the preparation of the environmental statement. An example might be information held by the Nature Conservancy Council about the ecology of a particular area, which could be relevant to the assessment of a project's likely effects.

29 It is up to the developer to approach the statutory consultees and indicate what sort of information would be helpful to him in preparing the environmental statement. The obligation on statutory consultees relates only to information already in their possession: they are not required to undertake research on behalf of the developer. Nor, at this stage, would consultees be expected to express a view about the merits of the proposal: their views on merits are invited at a later stage (see paragraph 37 below). Consultees may make a reasonable charge to cover the cost of making information requested by a developer available.

30 Developers should also consider whether to consult non-statutory bodies concerned with environmental issues, and the general public, during the preparation of the environmental statement. Bodies of these kinds may have particular knowledge and expertise to offer. Some are national organisations, for instance, the Royal Society for the Protection of Birds; in most areas there are also active local amenity societies and environmental groups. While developers are under no obligation to publicise their proposals before submitting a planning application, consultation with local amenity groups and with the general public can be useful in identifying key environmental issues, and may put the developer in a better position to modify the project in ways which would mitigate adverse effects and recognise local environmental concerns. It will also give the developer an early indication of the issues which are likely to be important issues at the formal application stage if, for instance, the proposal goes to public inquiry.

31 There is an extensive literature about how to assess the effects on the environment of particular processes and activities. The assessment techniques used, and the degree of detail in which any particular subject is treated in an environmental statement, will depend on the character of the proposal, the environment which it is likely to affect, and the information available. While a careful study of the proposed location will generally be needed (including environmental survey information), original scientific research will not normally be necessary. The local planning authority and statutory consultees may be able to advise the developer on sources of specialist information, for example, about particular local conditions.

32 Environmental statements will often need to recognise that there is some uncertainty attached to the prediction of environmental effects. Where there is uncertainty, it needs to be explicitly recognised. However, uncertainty is not in itself a reason for discounting the importance of particular potential environmental effects, simply because other effects can be more confidently predicted.

Submission of planning application and environmental statement

33 The planning application should be submitted in the normal way, accompanied by the completed environmental statement. It will be for the planning authority to judge how much information is required in the particular case, but the preparation of an environmental statement is bound to require the developer to work out his proposals in some detail; otherwise any thorough appraisal of likely effects will be impossible. Where an application is in outline, the planning authority will still need to have sufficient information on a project's likely effects to enable them to judge whether the development should take place or not. The information given in the environmental statement will have an important bearing on whether matters may be reserved in an outline permission: it will be important to ensure that the development does not take place in a form which would lead to significantly different effects from those considered at the planning application stage.

34 When submitting the planning application, the developer is required to publish a notice in a local newspaper and to post notices on the site indicating where and when the environmental statement may be inspected. The place should be in the locality of the project and the statement should be available for inspection at reasonable hours.

35 The developer is also required to provide the planning authority with sufficient copies of the environmental statement to enable one to be sent to each of the statutory consultees. Alternatively, the developer may send copies of the statement direct to the consultees. Where a consultee agrees, part only of the statement need be provided.

36 The developer should make a reasonable number of copies of the statement available for sale to members of the public. A reasonable charge reflecting printing and distribution costs may be made.

Handling by the planning authority

37 The planning authority will place the planning application on Part I of the Planning Register, together with the environmental statement. The authority and the developer may wish to consider the need for further publicity at this stage, for example, publication of further details of the project in a local newspaper, or an exhibition. The planning authority will also need to notify statutory consultees of the application (unless the developer has already done so) and invite them to comment on the environmental statement. Consultees must be allowed at least 14 days from receipt of the statement in which to comment before a decision is taken. It will often be useful for the planning authority to discuss the project with consultees who have a particular interest in its environmental effects before reaching their conclusions on the planning application.

38 The planning authority are also required to send a copy of the planning application and the environmental statement to the Secretary of State. This will assist the Department in monitoring and, in those exceptional circumstances where a proposed development is likely to have significant effects on the environment in another EC member state, will enable certain requirements of the Directive for exchange of information with other member states to be met.

Requests for further information

39 Where the planning authority consider that the information provided in the developer's environmental statement, together with that available to the authority from other sources, is insufficient to permit a proper evaluation of the project's likely environmental effects, the authority have power to require the provision of further information, or of evidence to verify the information that has already been provided. The use of these powers should not normally be necessary, especially if the parties have worked together during the

preparation of the environmental statement. Nevertheless, further consultation between the planning authority and the developer may be necessary at this stage, in particular to consider comments made by consultees, and possibly amendments to the proposal to meet objections that have been raised.

40 Where an authority consider that they do not have the necessary expertise to evaluate the information contained in an environmental statement, they may decide to employ consultants or other suitably qualified persons or organisations to advise them.

Determination of application

41 The planning authority are required to determine a planning application which is the subject of environmental assessment within 16 weeks, unless the developer agrees to a longer period. (Where the environmental statement is submitted after the planning application, the 16 week period runs from the authority's receipt of the statement.) In determining the application, the authority are of course required to have regard to the environmental statement, as well as to other material considerations. As with any other planning application, the planning authority may refuse permission or grant it with or without conditions.

42 The planning authority cannot take the view that a planning application is invalid because they consider that an inadequate environmental statement has been submitted. In that event, the planning authority should request the developer to supplement his initial statement under the powers referred to in paragraph 39 above. If the developer fails or is unable to do so, it will be for the planning authority to decide whether to refuse permission. If so, or if the authority fail to make a decision within the 16 week period referred to above, the developer will have the normal right of appeal to the Secretary of State.

Appeals and call-ins

43 The right of appeal to the Secretary of State against an adverse decision by a planning authority (or against an authority's failure to determine an application within the 16 week time limit) is the same for planning applications to which the EA Regulations apply as for other applications. Similarly, the Secretary of State's power to call in a planning application applies also in these cases. Where an environmental statement has been prepared to accompany a planning application, the information which it contains will be among the material considerations which an Inspector will

take into account in considering an appeal. The Secretary of State and his Inspectors, like the planning authority, have power to request the developer to provide further information where they consider that the environmental statement is inadequate as it stands. Any additional information provided by the developer in response to such a request will be made available to all parties to an appeal.

Flow charts

44 Appendix 6 to the booklet provides illustrative flow charts for the 3 main procedural stages, ie. application to the planning authority for an opinion on the need for EA; application to the Secretary of State for a direction where a developer disagrees with the planning authority's opinion that EA is required; and submission of an environmental statement to the planning authority in conjunction with a planning application.

Further background

45 Readers who wish to know more about the background to the introduction of EA into UK planning procedures may find it helpful to consult two recent collections of essays: *Environmental Impact Assessment: Theory and Practice*, ed. Peter Wathern (Unwin Hyman, London 1988); and *The Role of Environmental Impact Assessment in the Planning Process*, ed. Michael Clark and John Herington (Mansell Publishing Ltd, London, 1988).

PART III

ARRANGEMENTS FOR OTHER PROJECTS

46 The advice given in Parts I and II of this booklet is generally applicable to all projects. However, those Parts specifically describe the arrangements for environmental assessment by reference to the provisions applying to projects arising in England and Wales which are approved through the planning system. Part III gives brief guidance on the provisions for environmental assessment applying to other projects. More detailed guidance has been published separately for some of these projects (see Appendix 8, paragraph 4).

A: PROJECTS WHICH ARE NOT SUBJECT TO PLANNING CONTROL

Trunk roads and motorways

47 Motorways and other trunk roads in England and Wales (ie roads for which the Secretary of State for Transport or the Secretary of State for Wales is the highway authority) are approved under procedures set out in the Highways Act 1980. The Department concerned will normally consult the public widely about a number of alternative routes before selecting a preferred route for a new road. Once the preferred route has been announced, detailed design work is carried out leading to the publication of statutory orders. In most cases these orders will be the subject of a public inquiry held by an independent Inspector.

48 The Highways (Assessment of Environmental Effects) Regulations 1988 (SI No 1241) require the Secretary of State to publish an environmental statement for the preferred route at the time when the draft orders are published. The requirement applies to all new motorways and to trunk roads which are over 10 km in length or which are longer than 1 km where the route passes through or within 100 m of a sensitive area, i.e.:

    i a national park;

    ii a site of special scientific interest;

    iii a conservation area;

    iv a national nature reserve; *or*

    v an urban area (where 1,500 or more dwellings lie within 100m of the centre line of the proposed road).

In addition, environmental statements are required for other trunk road improvements which are likely to have a significant effect upon the environment; in determining whether a road proposal requires EA the Secretary of State will have regard to the criteria set out in DOE Circular 15/88 (Welsh Office Circular 23/88).

49 Where a road will lie either in or within 100m of certain environmentally sensitive areas, certain statutory bodies will be consulted before the project is initiated. These are as follows: the Countryside Commission for national parks and national nature reserves; the Nature Conservancy Council for national nature reserves and other sites of special scientific interest; and the relevant local planning authority for conservation areas. Non-statutory environmental bodies may also be consulted, where appropriate. The environmental statement will be published and both the statement and comments received on it will be a material consideration before the inquiry.

50 Roads developed by local authorities, and also roads developed by private developers, require planning permission and the provisions described in Parts I and II of this booklet apply to such roads.

Power stations, overhead power lines and long distance oil and gas pipelines

51 Under present electricity legislation, power stations and overhead electric lines (other than service lines) proposed by the Central Electricity Generating Board and the Area Electricity Boards are approved by the Secretary of State for Energy. The relevant procedures require local planning authorities and other persons to be consulted about the application and provide for a public inquiry to be held into it where appropriate.

52 Oil and gas pipelines of more than 10 miles in length require the authorisation of the Secretary of State for Energy under section 1 of the Pipelines Act 1962. The authorisation procedure also requires the Secretary of State to consult with local authorities and other bodies about a pipeline proposal and where appropriate to hold an inquiry.

53 Under the Electricity and Pipe-line Works (Assessment of Environmental Effects) Regulations 1989 (SI No 167) an environmental statement must be submitted to the Secretary of State for Energy in connection with applications which are made to him for:

i the construction or extension of a nuclear power station;

ii the construction or extension of a non-nuclear generating station with a heat output of 300 megawatts or more;

iii the construction or extension of a non-nuclear generating station with a heat output of less than 300 megawatts where the Secretary of State is of the view that the development would be likely to have significant effects upon the environment; and

iv the placement on land of an overhead line or the construction or diversion of a pipe-line of 10 miles or more in length, where the Secretary of State takes the view that the project concerned would be likely to have significant environmental effects.

The existence of the environmental statement must be advertised in the local press for the area concerned and, as well as identifying the site, must indicate where copies of the statement may be obtained.

54 Power stations proposed by private developers (apart from any nuclear power station) and oil and gas pipelines under 10 miles in length are approved under planning legislation and the provisions described in Parts I and II of this booklet apply to such proposals.

55 Under the Electricity Act 1989 changes will be made to arrangements for approving the construction or extension of power stations. When the relevant provisions of the Act are brought into force, the Secretary of State for Energy's consent will be necessary for the construction or extension of any power station with a capacity of 50 megawatts or more. Any smaller power station, however, will fall to be approved under planning legislation. Some changes of a minor nature will also be made in the arrangements for approving the installation of overhead power lines. Appropriate changes will be made to SI 1988 No. 1199 and SI 1989 No. 167 to reflect these new arrangements.

Afforestation

56 The Environmental Assessment (Afforestation) Regulations 1988 (SI No 1207) require environmental assessment of an afforestation project before grant may be given in any case where, in the opinion of the Forestry Commission, the project will be likely to have significant effects on the environment, and may lead to adverse ecological changes, by reason of factors such as its nature, size or location. Applicants for grant are strongly recommended to read the Forestry Commission's guidance leaflet* on the application of EA to forestry projects. This describes the detailed procedures for dealing with EA, the right of appeal against the requirement for EA, the preparation of an environmental statement, the arrangements for consultation and publicity, and the consideration of grant applications which require EA.

57 The Forestry Commission has indicated that it will generally require EA for new planting in a national nature reserve or a site of special scientific interest where such an operation is listed as potentially damaging. It will also look particularly carefully at the need for EA where planting is proposed in other areas of environmental importance, namely: National Parks, national scenic areas, areas of outstanding natural beauty and environmentally sensitive areas. EA will certainly be required where more than 100 hectares is proposed for planting within such designated areas. In cases of

*Forestry Commission booklet 'Environmental Assessment of Afforestation Projects', 4 August 1988.

doubt the Commission will seek the advice of the appropriate environmental agency before reaching a decision. The Forestry Commission will give its opinion in writing on whether EA is required within 4 weeks of receiving an application, unless the applicant agrees to a longer period. The regulations also provide a procedure which enables a potential applicant to apply to the Commission for a ruling on whether EA is needed in advance of submitting an application.

58 Where the Forestry Commission express the opinion that EA is required, the applicant should, within 4 weeks, write to the Commission either accepting the opinion or indicating an intention to appeal to the appropriate Forestry Minister (in England, the Minister of Agriculture, Fisheries and Food; in Scotland and Wales, the respective Secretaries of State). The regulations also provide for Ministers to call for EA where the Commission has decided otherwise. When it has been decided that EA is to be undertaken, the Commission will give notice of this decision to the Nature Conservancy Council, the Countryside Commission (or the Countryside Commission for Scotland, as appropriate) and any local authority, public authority or statutory body which appears to have an interest in the project concerned. These bodies will be asked to provide the applicant with any information in their possession which they or the applicant consider is relevant to the preparation of the environmental statement.

59. Where EA is required, the applicant for grant must provide an environmental statement, which must be publicised by notices in at least 2 local newspapers, and allow the public to comment, in writing, to the Commission. Details of the project and copies of the environmental statement will be made available for inspection at Forestry Commission offices, or other convenient locations, and details of where copies of statements can be obtained or purchased must also be provided. At the same time the Commission will implement standard consultation procedures, as agreed with local authorities and statutory authorities, before deciding the application. The Commission will inform the applicant and those persons, statutory bodies or public authorities who made representations, of their decision on whether or not to admit the grant application. They will also publicise the decision.

Land drainage improvements

60 New land drainage works, including flood defence works and defences against the sea, require planning permission and the provisions described in Parts I and II of this booklet apply to such works. Improvements to existing

land drainage works undertaken by drainage bodies and the National Rivers Authority are permitted development specified in Parts 14 and 15 respectively of Schedule 2 to the Town and Country Planning General Development Order 1988 so that they do not require an express grant of planning permission. Under the Land Drainage Improvement Works (Assessment of Environmental Effects) Regulations 1988 (SI No. 1217), a drainage body shall consider whether or not the proposed works would be likely to have significant environmental effects and ought therefore to be the subject of an environmental statement. Their decision as to whether or not they propose to prepare an environmental statement will be advertised in at least two local newspapers, and the advertisement will include a description of the nature, size and location of the works. Where an environmental statement has been prepared, the drainage body will give notice in at least two local newspapers stating where and at what times copies of the statement may be inspected by members of the public. Copies of the statement will be sent to the Nature Conservancy Council, the Countryside Commission and any other authority or organisation which might have an interest in the matter, as well as to interested members of the public on request.

61 There is provision for representations to be made in the 28-day period following both types of advertisement. Where representations are received, these and the proposals for the works will be referred to the Minister of Agriculture, Fisheries and Food (for works in England) or to the Secretary of State for Wales (for works in Wales) for his direction. In respect of a decision by a drainage body not to prepare an environmental statement, the Minister or Secretary of State will direct whether an environmental statement should be prepared. Where an environmental statement has been prepared, and where a drainage body having received objections which have not been withdrawn wishes to proceed with the works, the Minister or Secretary of State will direct whether, and to what extent, the proposed works should proceed.

Ports and harbours

62 The Harbour Works (Assessment of Environmental Effects) Regulations 1988 (SI No. 1336) amend the Harbours Act 1964 in respect of applications for harbour revision orders or harbour empowerment orders made to the Minister of Agriculture, Fisheries and Food or to the Secretary of State for Transport (in Wales, to the Secretary of State for Wales) by developers who wish to undertake works. The relevant Minister will decide whether EA is needed ie, if the project falls either within Annex I to the Directive or within

Annex II and is likely to have significant environmental effects. If EA is required, the Minister will require the developer to submit an environmental statement in accordance with Annex III to the Directive. The completed statement must be published and the Nature Conservancy Council, the Countryside Commission, Her Majesty's Inspectorate of Pollution and the relevant local authority invited to comment on the proposals. Representations received in response to these consultations will then be considered by the Minister when he decides whether or not the proposed works should proceed. The Minister's decision will then be published.

63 The Harbour Works (Assessment of Environmental Effects) (No. 2) Regulations 1989 (SI No. 424) concern harbour works which are not covered by the above and which do not require planning permission. Applications made under the Coast Protection Act 1949 and notices under more recent legislation are scrutinised by the appropriate Minister (ie the Secretary of State for Transport or, for fisheries harbours or marine works, the Minister of Agriculture, Fisheries and Food or the Secretary of State for Scotland or Wales, as appropriate) who will then decide if the proposed works require EA under the terms of the Directive. If the Minister decides that EA is necessary, he will direct the developer to submit an environmental statement in accordance with Annex III to the Directive. The developer must publish a notice in a local newspaper and at the premises of the harbour authority concerned giving details of the proposals, the requirement for EA, where copies of the application and environmental statement may be inspected, how they may be obtained and how representations may be made. The Minister concerned may also direct the developer to supply copies of the environmental statement to the appropriate local planning authority, the Countryside Commission, the Nature Conservancy Council and Her Majesty's Inspectorate of Pollution and require the proposals to be considered at a public inquiry. In coming to a decision on whether or not the proposed works should proceed the Minister will have regard to the environmental statement, any representations that have been received from the above-mentioned consultees and the public and the report of the inquiry, if one is held. The Minister's decision (giving his reasons and the considerations involved) will be notified to the developer and all those who made representations or who were consulted.

Marine salmon farming

64 Developments of on-shore salmon farming facilities may require planning permission and the provisions described in Parts I and II of this booklet apply to proposals for such facilities. Off-shore facilities do not require planning permission but require a lease from the Crown Estate Commissioners. The Environmental Assessment (Salmon Farming in Marine Waters) Regulations

1988 (SI No. 1218), which apply to England, Scotland and Wales, require the Commissioners, before granting such a lease in circumstances where the development may have significant effects on the environment, to consider an environmental statement provided by the developer and comments on it from consultees and the general public. The Commissioners have issued guidance* indicating the broad criteria against which they will determine whether to require the provision of an environmental statement. The Commissioners must inform consultees (eg the Nature Conservancy Council or the Countryside Commission) of any requirement for EA, and publish a notice in a local newspaper and the London or Edinburgh Gazette giving details of where the submitted environmental statement may be inspected or obtained and inviting the public to make written representations. The consultees must also be invited to comment on the environmental statement. The applicant and consultees will then be informed of the decision on the proposal by the Crown Estate Commissioners.

Marine dredging for minerals

65 Dredging for minerals off-shore does not require planning permission but requires a dredging licence from the Crown Estate Commissioners. Before granting licences, the Commissioners seek the views of interested bodies and request a 'Government view' from the relevant co-ordinating Government Department (either the Department of the Environment, the Scottish Development Department or the Welsh Office). In cases where dredging is likely to have significant environmental effects, the applicant is required to provide an environmental statement which is made available to the bodies consulted under the Government view procedure. The Commissioners have drawn up indicative criteria for identifying such cases which include applications relating to areas of shallow water or fish spawning grounds or which are near to marine nature reserves. The need for environmental assessment in any case is determined by the Commissioners in consultation with the Department of the Environment, the Scottish Development Department or the Welsh Office.

B. PROJECTS ARISING IN SCOTLAND AND NORTHERN IRELAND

66 The arrangements for environmental assessment in Scotland are broadly similar to those applying in England and Wales. The guidance in this booklet is therefore generally applicable to Scottish projects. However, there are

*'Environmental Assessment of Marine Salmon Farms', Crown Estate Office, Edinbugh, 15 July 1988.

some differences on account of the different legal and administrative arrangements which apply in Scotland. The Environmental Assessment (Scotland) Regulations 1988 (SI No. 1221) include provisions equivalent to the regulations already described which apply to projects requiring planning permission (Parts I and II of this booklet), roads (paragraphs 47 to 50 above), power stations and overhead lines (paragraphs 51 to 55 above) and land drainage improvements (paragraphs 60 and 61 above). Scottish Development Department Circular 13/88 explains these provisions. The arrangements for environmental assessments in SPZs and EZs in Scotland are explained in SDD Circular 26/88. Copies of these circulars can be obtained from the Scottish Development Department, Planning Division, Room 6/86, New St Andrew's House, Edinburgh EH1 3SZ.

67 Because of the different legal and administrative arrangements in Northern Ireland, separate provision for environmental assessment is being made there. However, the general principles described in this booklet hold good. Details of the provisions which apply to particular kinds of project in Northern Ireland may be obtained from the Department of the Environment (Northern Ireland), Commonwealth House, 35 Castle Street, Belfast BT1 1GU.

C. PROJECTS APPROVED BY PRIVATE ACT OF PARLIAMENT

68 Under article 1.5 of the Directive, the Directive does not apply to projects the details of which are approved by a specific act of national legislation. This provision serves to exempt projects which are authorised by a private or hybrid Bill. It is the Government's view that where, but for this provision, environmental assessment would have been required for a project, the promoter of a Bill should provide an environmental statement which can be considered by the select and standing committees of each House on the Bill. The Government will ensure that it will provide such statements in connection with hybrid Bills relating to a project which, but for article 1.5, would require environmental assessment.

69 The Joint Select Committee on Private Bill procedure proposed in their report published in the autumn of 1988* that each House of Parliament should amend its standing orders to require an environmental statement to be deposited with any Bill to approve a project which would require assessment under the Directive but for article 1.5. The Committee envisaged procedures under which the Department of the Environment and other Departments would determine whether environmental assessment is in fact necessary and would later report on the environmental statements which

---

* Report of the Joint Committee on Private Bill Procedure together with the Proceedings of the Committee and Minutes of Evidence, HL Paper 97 (HC 625), HMSO £15.90, 20 July 1988.

promoters would be required to submit to Parliament. The Government support the Committee's recommendation and are willing for Government Departments to undertake the functions envisaged for them. They are consulting with the authorities in each House about the way in which those aspects of the recommendation which would affect procedures outside Parliament can best be implemented.

APPENDIX 1

Schedule 1 projects

The following types of development ('Schedule 1 projects') require environmental assessment in every case:

(1) The carrying out of building or other operations, or the change of use of buildings or other land (where a material change) to provide any of the following—

1 A crude-oil refinery (excluding an undertaking manufacturing only lubricants from crude oil) or an installation for the gasification and liquefaction of 500 tonnes or more of coal or bituminous shale per day.

2 A thermal power station or other combustion installation with a heat output of 300 megawatts or more, other than a nuclear power station or other nuclear reactor.

3 An installation designed solely for the permanent storage or final disposal of radioactive waste.

4 An integrated works for the initial melting of cast-iron and steel.

5 An installation for the extraction of asbestos or for the processing and transformation of asbestos or products containing asbestos:

   (a) where the installation produces asbestos-cement products, with an annual production of more than 20,000 tonnes of finished products; or

   (b) where the installation produces friction material, with an annual production of more than 50 tonnes of finished products; or

   (c) in other cases, where the installation will utilise more than 200 tonnes of asbestos per year.

6 An integrated chemical installation, that is to say, an industrial installation or group of installations where two or more linked chemical or physical processes are employed for the manufacture of olefins from petroleum products, or of sulphuric acid, nitric acid, hydrofluoric acid, chlorine or fluorine.

7 A special road; a line for long-distance railway traffic; or an aerodrome with a basic runway length of 2,100 m or more.

8 A trading port, an inland waterway which permits the passage of vessels of over 1,350 tonnes or a port for inland waterway traffic capable of handling such vessels.

9 A waste-disposal installation for the incineration or chemical treatment of special waste.

(2) The carrying out of operations whereby land is filled with special waste, or the change of use of land (where a material change) to use for the deposit of such waste.

Schedule 2 projects

The following types of development ('Schedule 2 projects') require environmental assessment if they are likely to have significant effects on the environment by virtue of factors such as their nature, size or location:

1. Agriculture

(a) water-management for agriculture
(b) poultry-rearing
(c) pig-rearing
(d) a salmon hatchery
(e) an installation for the rearing of salmon
(f) the reclamation of land from the sea

2. Extractive industry

(a) extracting peat
(b) deep drilling, including in particular—
   (i) geothermal drilling
   (ii) drilling for the storage of nuclear waste material
   (iii) drilling for water supplies
        but excluding drilling to investigate the stability of the soil
(c) extracting minerals (other than metalliferous and energy-producing minerals) such as marble, sand, gravel, shale, salt, phosphates and potash
(d) extracting coal or lignite by underground or open-cast mining
(e) extracting petroleum
(f) extracting natural gas
(g) extracting ores
(h) extracting bituminous shale
(i) extracting minerals (other than metalliferous and energy-producing minerals) by open-cast mining
(j) a surface industrial installation for the extraction of coal, petroleum, natural gas or ores or bituminous shale
(k) a coke oven (dry distillation of coal)
(l) an installation for the manufacture of cement

3. Energy industry

(a) a non-nuclear thermal power station, not being an installation falling within Schedule 1, or an installation for the production of electricity, steam and hot water
(b) an industrial installation for carrying gas, steam or hot water; or the transmission of electrical energy by overhead cables
(c) the surface storage of natural gas
(d) the underground storage of combustible gases
(e) the surface storage of fossil fuels
(f) the industrial briquetting of coal or lignite
(g) an installation for the production or enrichment of nuclear fuels
(h) an installation for the reprocessing of irradiated nuclear fuels
(i) an installation for the collection or processing of radioactive waste, not being an installation falling within Schedule 1
(j) an installation for hydroelectric energy production

4. Processing of metals

(a) an ironworks or steelworks including a foundry, forge, drawing plant or rolling mill (not being a works falling within Schedule 1)
(b) an installation for the production (including smelting, refining, drawing and rolling) of non-ferrous metals, other than precious metals
(c) the pressing, drawing or stamping of large castings
(d) the surface treatment and coating of metals
(e) boilermaking or manufacturing reservoirs, tanks and other sheet-metal containers
(f) manufacturing or assembling motor vehicles or manufacturing motor-vehicle engines
(g) a shipyard
(h) an installation for the construction or repair of aircraft
(i) the manufacture of railway equipment
(j) swaging by explosives
(k) an installation for the roasting or sintering of metallic ores

5. Glass making

the manufacture of glass

6. Chemical industry

(a) the treatment of intermediate products and production of chemicals, other than development falling within Schedule 1
(b) the production of pesticides or pharmaceutical products, paints or varnishes, elastomers or peroxides
(c) the storage of petroleum or petrochemical or chemical products

7. Food industry

(a) the manufacture of vegetable or animal oils or fats
(b) the packing or canning of animal or vegetable products
(c) the manufacture of dairy products
(d) brewing or malting
(e) confectionery or syrup manufacture
(f) an installation for the slaughter of animals
(g) an industrial starch manfacturing installation
(h) a fish-meal or fish-oil factory
(i) a sugar factory

8. Textile, leather, wood and paper industries

(a) a wool scouring, degreasing and bleaching factory
(b) the manufacture of fibre board, particle board or plywood
(c) the manufacture of pulp, paper or board
(d) a fibre-dyeing factory
(e) a cellulose-processing and production installation
(f) a tannery or a leather dressing factory

9. Rubber industry

the manufacture and treatment of elastomer-based products

10. Infrastructure projects

(a) an industrial estate development project
(b) an urban development project
(c) a ski-lift or cable-car
(d) the construction of a road, or a harbour, including a fishing harbour, or an aerodrome, not being development falling within Schedule 1
(e) canalisation or flood-relief works
(f) a dam or other installation designed to hold water or store it on a long-term basis
(g) a tramway, elevated or underground railway, suspended line or similar line, exclusively or mainly for passenger transport
(h) an oil or gas pipeline installation
(i) a long-distance aqueduct
(j) a yacht marina

11. Other projects

(a) a holiday village or hotel complex
(b) a permanent racing or test track for cars or motor cycles
(c) an installation for the disposal of controlled waste or waste from mines and quarries, not being an installation falling within Schedule 1
(d) a waste water treatment plant
(e) a site for depositing sludge
(f) the storage of scrap iron
(g) a test bench for engines, turbines or reactors
(h) the manufacture of artificial mineral fibres
(i) the manufacture, packing, loading or placing in cartridges of gunpowder or other explosives
(j) a knackers' yard

12. The modification of a development which has been carried out, where that development is within a description mentioned in Schedule 1.

13. Development within a description mentioned in Schedule 1, where it is exclusively or mainly for the development and testing of new methods or products and will not be permitted for longer than one year.

1 This appendix reproduces the guidance given to local planning authorities in DOE Circular 15/88 (Welsh Office Circular 23/88) on factors which may indicate a need for environmental assessment of Schedule 2 projects.

2 It should be borne in mind that the fundamental test to be applied in each case is the likelihood of significant environmental effects. Regard should be had to the advice given in this booklet and in the Circular.

Agriculture

1 *New pig rearing installations* will not generally require EA: however, those designed to house more than 400 sows or 5,000 fattening pigs may require EA.

2 *New poultry rearing installations* will not generally require EA: however, those designed to house more than 100,000 broilers or 50,000 layers, turkeys or other poultry may require EA.

3 *Salmon farming.* Both salmon hatcheries and installations for the rearing of salmon are listed in Schedule 2. The need for EA for such developments will depend on the environmental effects generally and also on the particular implications for a river system: however, smaller developments designed to produce less than 100 tonnes of fish a year should not normally require EA.

4 *New drainage and flood defence works* may merit EA where it emerges from the consultations between drainage bodies and environmental interests (in order to comply with their obligations under section 22 of the Water Act 1973, as amended by section 48 of the Wildlife and Countryside Act 1981) that the project in question is likely to have a significant environmental effect. In disputed cases the Secretary of State will decide on the need for EA after taking into account the views of the relevant Agriculture Minister in view of his statutory responsibilities under the Land Drainage Act 1976.

Extractive industry

5 Whether or not mineral workings would have significant environmental effects so as to require EA will depend upon such factors as the sensitivity of the location, size, working methods, the proposals for disposing of waste, the nature and extent of processing and ancillary operations and arrangements for transporting minerals away from the site. The duration of the proposed workings is also a factor to be taken into account.

6 It is established mineral planning policy that minerals applications in national parks and areas of outstanding natural beauty should be subject to the most rigorous examination, and this should generally include EA.

7 All new *deep mines*, apart from small mines, may merit EA. For *opencast coal mines* and *sand and gravel workings*, sites of more than 50 ha may well require EA and significantly smaller sites could require EA if they are in a sensitive area of if subjected to particularly obtrusive operations.

8 Whether *rock quarries* or *clay operations* or other mineral workings require EA will depend on the location and the scale and type of the activities proposed.

9 For *oil and gas extraction* the main considerations will be the volume of oil or gas to be produced, the arrangements for transporting it from the site and the sensitivity of the area affected. Where production is expected to be substantial (300 tonnes or more per day) or the site concerned is sensitive to disturbance from normal operations, EA may be necessary. *Exploratory deep drilling* would not normally require EA unless the site is in a sensitive location or unless the site is unusually sensitive to limited disturbance occurring over the short period involved. It would not be appropriate to require EA for exploratory activity simply because it might eventually lead to production of oil or gas.

Manufacturing industry

10 New manufacturing plants requiring sites in the range 20-30 ha or above may well require EA.

11 In addition, EA may occasionally be required for new manufacturing plants on account of expected discharge of waste, emission of pollutants, etc. Among the factors to be taken into account are the following:—

—whether the project involves a process designated as a 'scheduled process' for the purpose of air pollution control;

31

—whether the process involves discharges to water which require the consent of the water authority;

—whether the installation would give rise to the presence of environmentally significant quantities of potentially hazardous or polluting substances;

—whether the process would give rise to radioactive or other hazardous waste.

12 Whether or not a project involving such a process requires EA will depend on the location, nature and significance of the emissions, etc., involved: in forming a judgment on this local planning authorities may find it helpful to consult the relevant authorities (HMIP, HSE, the water authority or the environmental health authority). It should be noted that existing controls over hazardous and polluting substances will not be affected by the Regulations and the need for a consent under other legislation will *not* in itself be a justification for EA: authorities will need to consider with the relevant authority the likely significance, from the point of view of the possible need for EA, of the matters which give rise to the need for the consent.

Industrial estate development projects

13 Industrial estate developments may require EA where:—

(i) the site area of the estate is in excess of 20 ha; or

(ii) there are significant numbers of dwellings in close proximity to the site of the proposed estate, eg. more than 1,000 dwellings within 200 metres of the site boundaries.

Smaller estates might exceptionally require EA in sensitive urban or rural areas, particularly if associated with other works (eg. roads, canalisation projects, flood relief works) which are listed in Schedule 2.

14 Assessment of an industrial estate proposal as an infrastructure project will not necessarily remove the need for assessment of individual industrial installations to be provided within the estate. These might require EA if they fall within Schedule 2 and are likely to give rise to significant environmental effects which need to be appraised separately from the effects of the estate as a whole.

15 Redevelopment of previously developed land is unlikely to require EA unless the proposed use is one of the specific types of development listed in Schedules 1 or 2 (other than items 10(a) and 10(b)) or the project is on a very much greater scale than the previous use of the land.

16 The need for EA for new urban development schemes on sites which have not previously been intensively developed should be considered in the light of the sensitivity of the particular location. Such schemes (other than purely housing schemes) may require EA where:—

    (i) the site area of the scheme is more than 5 ha in an urbanised area; or

    (ii) there are significant numbers of dwellings in close proximity to the site of the proposed development, eg. more than 700 dwellings within 200 metres of the site boundaries; or

    (iii) the development would provide a total of more than 10,000 sq. metres (gross) of shops, offices or other commercial uses.

Proposals for high rise development (eg. over 50 metres) are not likely to be candidates for EA for that reason alone; but this may be an additional consideration where one or more of the above criteria is met.

17 Smaller urban development schemes may require EA in particularly sensitive areas, eg. central area redevelopment schemes in historic town centres. In this context conservation area designations, particularly if associated with high concentrations of listed buildings, should be taken into account in assessing the significance of a proposed development. In cases of doubt, HBMC (CADW in Wales) should be consulted on the need for EA in relation to projects affecting the built heritage. However, it should be borne in mind that the normal planning and listed building controls already ensure that the effects of development proposals on the built heritage are considered.

18 The need for EA in respect of proposals for major out-of-town shopping schemes should also be considered in the light of the sensitivity of the particular location. For such schemes a floor area threshold of about 20,000 sq. metres (gross) may provide an indication of significance (cf. paragraph 22 of Planning Policy Guidance Note No. 6).

Local roads

19 The construction of new motorways will require EA under Schedule 1. Outside urban areas, the construction of new roads and major road

improvements over 10 km in length, or over 1 km in length if the road passes through a national park or through or within 100 metres of a site of special scientific interest, a national nature reserve or a conservation area, may require EA.

20 Within urban areas, any scheme where more than 1,500 dwellings lie within 100 metres of the centre line of the proposed road (or of an existing road in the case of major improvements) may be a candidate for EA.

Airports

21 The construction of airports with a basic runway length of over 2,100 metres will require EA under Schedule 1. Smaller new airports will also generally require EA. EA may also be required for major works such as new runways or passenger terminals at larger airports, the original development of which would have required EA under Schedule 1.

Other infrastructure projects

22 A broad indication of likely environmental effect may be given by the land requirement for an infrastructure project. Projects requiring sites in excess of 100 ha may well be candidates for EA.

Waste disposal

23 Installations, including landfill sites, for the transfer, treatment or disposal of household, industrial and commercial wastes (as defined in the Collection and Disposal of Waste Regulations 1988) with a capacity of more than 75,000 tonnes a year may well be candidates for EA even when the special considerations relating to hazardous wastes (paragraph 11 above) do not arise. Except in the most sensitive locations, sites taking smaller tonnages of these wastes, Civic Amenity sites, and sites seeking only to accept inert wastes (demolition rubble, etc.) are unlikely to be candidates for EA.

REQUIREMENTS OF THE REGULATIONS AS TO THE CONTENT OF ENVIRONMENTAL STATEMENTS

The following are the statutory provisions with respect to the content of environmental statements, as set out in Schedule 3 to the Town and Country Planning (Assessment of Environmental Effects) Regulations 1988:

1. An environmental statement comprises a document or series of documents providing for the purpose of assessing the likely impact upon the environment of the development proposed to be carried out, the information specified in paragraph 2 (referred to in this Schedule as 'the specified information').

2. The specified information is—

(a) a description of the development proposed, comprising information about the site and the design and size or scale of the development;

(b) the data necessary to identify and assess the main effects which that development is likely to have on the environment;

(c) a description of the likely significant effects, direct and indirect, on the environment of the development, explained by reference to its possible impact on—

human beings;
flora;
fauna;
soil;
water;
air;
climate;
the landscape;
the inter-action between any of the foregoing;
material assets;
the cultural heritage;

(d) where significant adverse effects are identified with respect to any of the foregoing, a description of the measures envisaged in order to avoid, reduce or remedy those effects; and

(e) a summary in non-technical language of the information specified above.

3. An environmental statement may include, by way of explanation or amplification of any specified information, further information on any of the following matters—

(a) the physical characteristics of the proposed development, and the land-use requirements during the construction and operational phases;

(b) the main characteristics of the production processes proposed, including the nature and quantity of the materials to be used;

(c) the estimated type and quantity of expected residues and emissions (including pollutants of water, air or soil, noise, vibration, light, heat and radiation) resulting from the proposed development when in operation;

(d) (in outline) the main alternatives (if any) studied by the applicant, appellant or authority and an indication of the main reasons for choosing the development proposed, taking into account the environmental effects;

(e) the likely significant direct and indirect effects on the environment of the development proposed which may result from—

(i) the use of natural resources;

(ii) the emission of pollutants, the creation of nuisances, and the elimination of waste;

(f) the forecasting methods used to assess any effects on the environment about which information is given under subparagraph (e); and

(g) any difficulties, such as technical deficiencies or lack of know-how, encountered in compiling any specified information.

In paragraph (e), "effects" includes secondary, cumulative, short, medium and long term, permanent, temporary, positive and negative effects.

4. Where further information is included in an environmental statement pursuant to paragraph 3, a non-technical summary of that information shall also be provided.

APPENDIX 4

This checklist is intended as a guide to the subjects that need to be considered in the course of preparing an environmental statement. It is unlikely that all the items will be relevant to any one project. (See paragraphs 24 and 25 of the main text.)

The environmental effects of a development during its construction and commissioning phases should be considered separately from the effects arising whilst it is operational. Where the operational life of a development is expected to be limited, the effects of decommissioning or reinstating the land should also be considered separately.

Section 1

Information describing the project

1.1 Purpose and physical characteristics of the project, including details of proposed access and transport arrangements, and of numbers to be employed and where they will come from.

1.2 Land use requirements and other physical features of the project:

a during construction;

b when operational;

c after use has ceased (where appropriate).

1.3 Production processes and operational features of the project:

a type and quantities of raw materials, energy and other resources consumed;

b residues and emissions by type, quantity, composition and strength including:

i discharges to water;

ii emissions to air;

iii noise;

iv vibration;

v light;

vi heat;

viii radiation;

viii deposits/residues to land and soil;

ix others.

1.4 Main alternative sites and processes considered, where appropriate, and reasons for final choice.

Section 2

Information describing the site and its environment

Physical features

2.1 Population—proximity and numbers.

2.2 Flora and fauna (including both habitats and species)—in particular, protected species and their habitats.

2.3 Soil; agricultural quality, geology and geomorphology.

2.4 Water; aquifers, water courses, shoreline, including the type, quantity, composition and strength of any existing discharges.

2.5 Air; climatic factors, air quality, etc.

2.6 Architectural and historic heritage, archaeological sites and features, and other material assets.

2.7 Landscape and topography.

2.8 Recreational uses.

2.9 Any other relevant environmental features.

The policy framework

2.10 Where applicable, the information considered under this section should include all relevant statutory designations such as national nature reserves, sites of special scientific interest, national parks, areas of outstanding natural beauty, heritage coasts, regional parks, country parks, national forest parks and designated areas, local nature reserves, areas affected by tree preservation orders, water protection zones, nitrate sensitive areas, conservation areas, listed buildings, scheduled ancient monuments, and designated areas of archaeological importance. It should also include references to structure, unitary and local plan policies applying to the site and surrounding area which are relevant to the proposed development.

2.11 Reference should also be made to international designations, eg. those under the EC 'Wild Birds' Directive, the World Heritage Convention, the UNEP Man and Biosphere Programme and the Ramsar Convention.

Section 3

Assessment of effects

(Including direct and indirect, secondary, cumulative, short, medium and long-term, permanent and temporary, positive and negative effects of the project.)

Effects on human beings, buildings and man-made features

3.1 Change in population arising from the development, and consequential environment effects.

3.2 Visual effects of the development on the surrounding area and landscape.

3.3 Levels and effects of emissions from the development during normal operation.

3.4 Levels and effects of noise from the development.

3.5 Effects of the development on local roads and transport.

3.6 Effects of the development on buildings, the architectural and historic heritage, archaeological features, and other human artefacts, eg. through pollutants, visual intrusion, vibration.

Effects on flora, fauna and geology

3.7 Loss of, and damage to, habitats and plant and animal species.

3.8 Loss of, and damage to, geological, palaeontological and physiographic features.

3.9 Other ecological consequences.

Effects on land

3.10 Physical effects of the development, eg. change in local topography, effect of earth-moving on stability, soil erosion, etc.

3.11 Effects of chemical emissions and deposits on soil of site and surrounding land.

3.12 Land use/resource effects:

a quality and quantity of agricultural land to be taken;

b sterilisation of mineral resources;

c other alternative uses of the site, including the 'do nothing' option;

d effect on surrounding land uses including agriculture;

e waste disposal.

Effects on water

3.13 Effects of development on drainage pattern in the area.

3.14 Changes to other hydrographic characteristics, eg. ground water level, water courses, flow of underground water.

3.15 Effects on coastal or estuarine hydrology.

3.16 Effects of pollutants, waste, etc. on water quality.

Effects on air and climate

3.17 Level and concentration of chemical emissions and their environmental effects.

3.18 Particulate matter.

3.19 Offensive odours.

3.20 Any other climatic effects.

Other indirect and secondary effects associated with the project

3.21 Effects from traffic (road, rail, air, water) related to the development.

3.22 Effects arising from the extraction and consumption of materials, water, energy or other resources by the development.

3.23 Effects of other development associated with the project, eg. new roads, sewers, housing, power lines, pipelines, telecommunications, etc.

3.24 Effects of association of the development with other existing or proposed development.

3.25 Secondary effects resulting from the interaction of separate direct effects listed above.

Section 4

Mitigating measures

4.1 Where significant adverse effects are identified, a description of the measures to be taken to avoid, reduce or remedy those effects, eg:

    a site planning;

    b technical measures, eg:

        i process selection;

        ii recycling;

        iii pollution control and treatment;

        iv containment (eg, bunding of storage vessels).

    c aesthetic and ecological measures, eg:

        i mounding;

        ii design, colour, etc;

        iii landscaping;

        iv tree plantings;

        v measures to preserve particular habitats or create alternative habitats;

        vi recording of archaeological sites;

        vii measures to safeguard historic building or sites.

4.2 Assessment of the likely effectiveness of mitigating measures.

Section 5

Risks of accidents and hazardous development

5.1 Risks of accidents as such are not covered in the Directive on EA or, consequently, in the implementing Regulations. However, when the proposed development involves materials that could be harmful to the environment (including people) in the event of an accident, the environmental statement should include an indication of the preventive measures that will be adopted so that such an occurrence is not likely to have a significant effect. This could, where appropriate, include reference to compliance with the Health and Safety at Work Act 1974 and its relevant statutory provisions such as the Control of Industrial Major Accident Hazards Regulations 1984.

5.2 There are separate arrangements in force relating to the keeping or use of hazardous substances and the Health and Safety Executive provides local planning authorities with expert advice about risk assessment on any planning application involving a hazardous installation.

5.3 Nevertheless, it is desirable that wherever possible the risk of accident and the general environmental effects of developments should be considered together, and developers and planning authorities should bear this in mind.

LIST OF STATUTORY CONSULTEES WHERE ENVIRONMENTAL ASSESSMENT IS CARRIED OUT

(Regulation 8 of the Town and Country Planning (Assessment of Environmental Effects) Regulations 1988)

1 Any principal council for the area where the land is situated, if not the local planning authority.

2 The Countryside Commission.

3 The Nature Conservancy Council.

4 Her Majesty's Inspectorate of Pollution—for proposed developments which, in the opinion of the local planning authority, will:

    a involve mining operations, or manufacturing industry, or the disposal of waste; and

    b is likely either:

        i to give rise to waste, the disposal of which requires an authorisation under the Radioactive Substances Act 1960, or to discharges (other than of domestic sewage) which are controlled waste, or special waste, or are likely to require the licence or consent of a water authority; or

        ii to involve works specified in Schedule 1 to the Health and Safety (Emissions to the Atmosphere) Regulations 1983 (SI 1983 No.943).

5 Any body which the local planning authority would be required by article 18 of the Town and Country Planning General Development Order 1988 (SI 1988 No.1813) (or any direction under that article) to consult if the application were before them.

For ease of reference, article 18 of the 1988 GDO is reproduced below:

"Consultations before the grant of permission

18.—(1) Before granting permission for development which, in their opinion, falls within a category set out in the table below, a local planning authority shall consult the authority or person mentioned in relation to that category, except where—

(i) the local planning authority are the authority so mentioned;

(ii) the local planning authority are required to consult the authority so mentioned under articles 19 or 20; or

(iii) the authority or person so mentioned has advised the local planning authority that they do not wish to be consulted.

TABLE

Para	Description of Development	Consultee
(a)	Development likely to affect land in Greater London or in a metropolitan county	The local planning authority concerned
(b)	Development likely to affect land in a non-metropolitan county, other than land in a National Park	The district planning authority concerned
(c)	Development likely to affect land in a National Park	The county planning authority concerned
(d)	Development involving the manufacture, processing, keeping or use of a hazardous substance in such circumstances that there will at any one time be, or is likely to be, a notifiable quantity of such substance in, on, over or under any land	The Health and Safety Executive
(e)	Development likely to result in a material increase in the volume or a material change in the character of traffic—	
	(i) entering or leaving a trunk road; or	In England, the Secretary of State for Transport, in Wales the Secretary of State for Wales
	(ii) using a level crossing over a railway	The British Railways Board or other railway undertakers likely to be affected, and in England, the Secretary of State for Transport and, in Wales, the Secretary of State for Wales
(f)	Development likely to result in a material increase in the volume or a material change in the character of traffic entering or leaving a classified or proposed road	The local highway authority concerned

Para	Description of Development	Consultee
(g)	Development likely to prejudice the improvement or construction of a classified or proposed road	The local highway authority concerned
(h)	Development involving the formation, laying out or alteration of any means of access to a highway (other than a trunk road)	The local highway authority concerned
(i)	Development which involves the provision of a building or pipeline in an area of coal working notified by the British Coal Corporation to the local planning authority	The British Coal Corporation
(j)	Development involving or including mining operations	The National Rivers Authority (d)
(k)	Development involving or including the winning and working of coal by opencast methods	The Secretary of State for Energy
(l)	Development within three kilometres of Windsor Castle, Windsor Great Park, or Windsor Home Park, or within 800 metres of any other royal palace or park, which might affect the amenities (including security) of that palace or park	The Secretary of State for the Environment
(m)	Development of land in Greater London involving the demolition, in whole or part, or the material alteration of a listed building	The Historic Buildings and Monuments Commission
(n)	Development likely to affect the site of a scheduled ancient monument	In England, The Historic Buildings and Monuments Commission, in Wales, the Secretary of State for Wales
(o)	Development involving the carrying out of works or operations in the bed of or on the banks of a river or stream	The National Rivers Authority (d)
(p)	Development for the purpose of refining or storing mineral oils and their derivatives	The National Rivers Authority (d)
(q)	Development involving the use of land for the deposit of refuse or waste	The National Rivers Authority (d)

Para	Description of Development	Consultee
(r)	Development relating to the retention, treatment or disposal of sewage, trade-waste, slurry or sludge (other than the laying of sewers, the construction of pumphouses in a line of sewers, the construction of septic tanks and cesspools serving single dwelling-houses or single caravans or single buildings in which not more than ten people will normally reside, work or congregate, and works ancillary thereto)	The National Rivers Authority (d)
(s)	Development relating to the use of land as a cemetery	The National Rivers Authority (d)
(t)	Development in an area of special scientific interest of which notification has been given or has effect as if given to the local planning authority by the Nature Conservancy Council in accordance with section 28 of the Wildlife and Countryside Act 1981(**a**)	The Nature Conservancy Council
(u)	Development involving any land on which there is a theatre as defined in the Theatres Trust Act 1976(**b**)	The Theatres Trust
(v)	Development which is not for agricultural purposes and is not in accordance with the provisions of a development plan and involves— (i) the loss of not less than 20 hectares of grades 1, 2 or 3a agricultural land which is for the time being used (or was last used) for agricultural purposes; or (ii) the loss of less than 20 hectares of grades 1, 2 or 3a agricultural land which is for the time being used (or was last used) for agricultural purposes, in circumstances in which the development is likely to lead to a further loss of agricultural land amounting cumulatively to 20 hectares or more	In England, the Minister of Agriculture, Fisheries and Food and in Wales, the Secretary of State for Wales
(w)	Development within 250 metres of land which— (i) is or has, at any time in the 30 years before the relevant application, been used for the deposit of refuse or waste; and (ii) has been notified to the local planning authority by the waste disposal authority for the purposes of this provision	The waste disposal authority concerned

(**a**) 1981 c.69.
(**b**) 1976 c.27.
(**c**) Established by Schedule 1 to the Waste Regulation and Disposal (Authorities) Order 1985 (SI 1985/1884).
(**d**) As amended by the Town and Country Planning General Development (Amendment) (No.2) Order 1989 (SI 1989/1590).

(2) In paragraph (1)(w) "waste disposal authority" means—

    (a) in the area of the London Waste Regulation Authority, the Greater Manchester Waste Disposal Authority or the Merseyside Waste Disposal Authority(a) respectively, that authority;

    (b) elsewhere in England, the county council or metropolitan district council; or

    (c) in Wales, the district council.

(3) The Secretary of State may give directions to a local planning authority requiring that authority to consult with any person or body named in the directions, in any case or class of case specified in the directions.

(4) Where, by or under this article, a local planning authority are required to consult any person or body ("the consultee") before granting planning permission—

    (a) they shall, unless an applicant has served a copy of an application for planning permission on the consultee, give notice of the application to the consultee; and

    (b) they shall not determine the application until at least 14 days after the date on which notice is given under paragraph (a), or if earlier, 14 days after the date of service of a copy of the application on the consultee by the applicant.

(5) The local planning authority shall, in determining the application, take into account any representations received from a consultee.''

APPENDIX 6

FLOW CHARTS ILLUSTRATING THE MAIN PROCEDURAL STAGES

CHART 1:

APPLICATION BY DEVELOPER TO LOCAL PLANNING AUTHORITY FOR OPINION
ON NEED FOR ENVIRONMENTAL ASSESSMENT

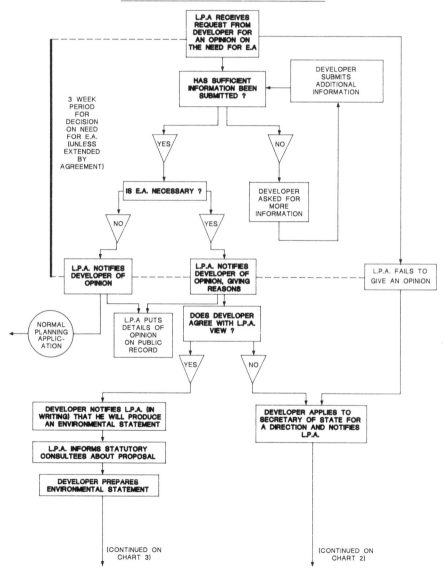

CHART 2:

APPLICATION TO SECRETARY OF STATE FOR DIRECTION WHERE DEVELOPER DISAGREES WITH LOCAL PLANNING AUTHORITY'S OPINION

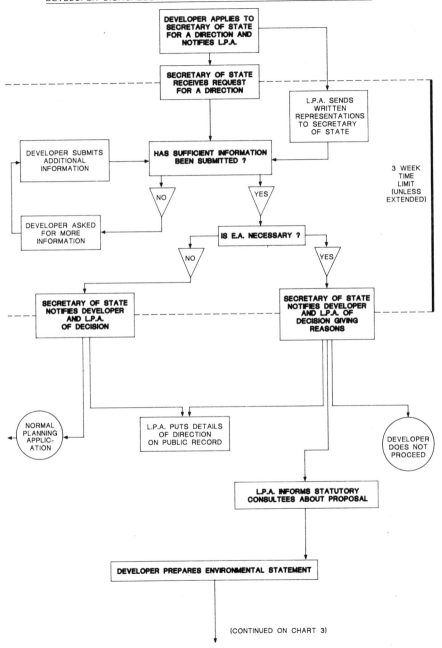

SUBMISSION OF ENVIRONMENTAL STATEMENT TO LOCAL PLANNING AUTHORITY
IN CONJUNCTION WITH PLANNING APPLICATION

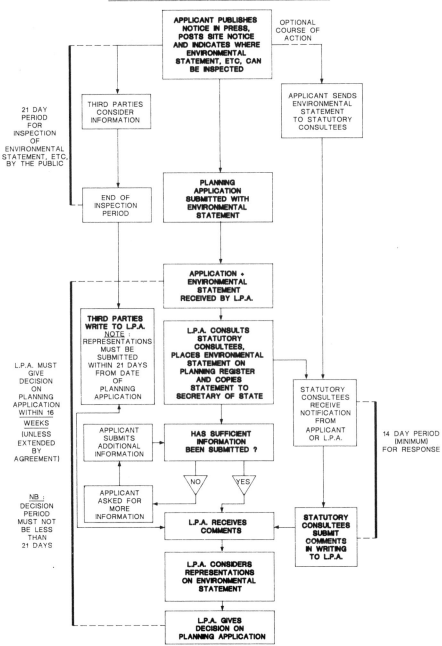

COUNCIL DIRECTIVE
of 27 June 1985
on the assessment of the effects of certain public and private projects on the environment

(85/337/EEC)

THE COUNCIL OF THE EUROPEAN COMMUNITIES,

Having regard to the Treaty establishing the European Economic Community, and in particular Articles 100 and 235 thereof,

Having regard to the proposal from the Commission[1],

Having regard to the opinion of the European Parliament[2],

Having regard to the opinion of the Economic and Social Committee[3],

Whereas the 1973[4] and 1977[5] action programmes of the European Communities on the environment, as well as the 1983[6] action programme, the main outlines of which have been approved by the Council of the European Communities and the representatives of the Governments of the Member States, stress that the best environmental policy consists in preventing the creation of pollution or nuisances at source, rather than subsequently trying to counteract their effects; whereas they affirm the need to take effects on the environment into account at the earliest possible stage in all the technical planning and decision-making processes; whereas to that end, they provide for the implementation of procedures to evaluate such effects;

Whereas the disparities between the laws in force in the various Member States with regard to the assessment of the environmental effects of public and private projects may create unfavourable competitive conditions and thereby directly affect the functioning of the common market; whereas, therefore, it is necessary to approximate national laws in this field pursuant to Article 100 of the Treaty;

Whereas, in addition, it is necessary to achieve one of the Community's objectives in the sphere of the protection of the environment and the quality of life;

Whereas, since the Treaty has not provided the powers required for this end, recourse should be had to Article 235 of the Treaty;

Whereas general principles for the assessment of environmental effects should be introduced with a view to supplementing and coordinating development consent procedures governing public and private projects likely to have a major effect on the environment;

[1] OJ No C 169, 9. 7. 1980, p. 14.
[2] OJ No C 66, 15. 3. 1982, p. 89.
[3] OJ No C 185, 27. 7. 1981, p. 8.
[4] OJ No C 112, 20. 12. 1973, p. 1.
[5] OJ No C 139, 13. 6. 1977, p. 1.
[6] OJ No C 46, 17. 2. 1983, p. 1.

Whereas development consent for public and private projects which are likely to have significant effects on the environment should be granted only after prior assessment of the likely significant environmental effects of these projects has been carried out; whereas this assessment must be conducted on the basis of the appropriate information supplied by the developer, which may be supplemented by the authorities and by the people who may be concerned by the project in question;

Whereas the principles of the assessment of environmental effects should be harmonized, in particular with reference to the projects which should be subject to assessment, the main obligations of the developers and the content of the assessment;

Whereas projects belonging to certain types have significant effects on the environment and these projects must as a rule be subject to systematic assessment;

Whereas projects of other types may not have significant effects on the environment in every case and whereas these projects should be assessed where the Member States consider that their characteristics so require;

Whereas, for projects which are subject to assessment, a certain minimal amount of information must be supplied, concerning the project and its effects;

Whereas the effects of a project on the environment must be assessed in order to take account of concerns to protect human health, to contribute by means of a better environment to the quality of life, to ensure maintenance of the diversity of species and to maintain the reproductive capacity of the ecosystem as a basic resource for life;

Whereas, however, this Directive should not be applied to projects the details of which are adopted by a specific act of national legislation, since the objectives of this Directive, including that of supplying information, are achieved through the legislative process;

Whereas, furthermore, it may be appropriate in exceptional cases to exempt a specific project from the assessment procedures laid down by this Directive, subject to appropriate information being supplied to the Commission.

HAS ADOPTED THIS DIRECTIVE:

Article 1

1. This Directive shall apply to the assessment of the environmental effects of those public and private projects which are likely to have significant effects on the environment.

2. For the purposes of this Directive:

'project' means:

—the execution of construction works or of other installations or schemes,

—other interventions in the natural surroundings and landscape including those involving the extraction of mineral resources;

'developer' means:

the applicant for authorization for a private project or the public authority which initiates a project;

'development consent' means:

the decision of the competent authority or authorities which entitles the developer to proceed with the project.

3. The competent authority or authorities shall be that or those which the Member States designate as responsible for performing the duties arising from this Directive.

4. Projects serving national defence purposes are not covered by this Directive.

5. This Directive shall not apply to projects the details of which are adopted by a specific act of national legislation, since the objectives of this Directive, including that of supplying information, are achieved through the legislative process.

Article 2

1. Member States shall adopt all measures necessary to ensure that, before consent is given, projects likely to have significant effects on the environment by virtue *inter alia*, of their nature, size or location are made subject to an assessment with regard to their effects.

These projects are defined in Article 4.

2. The environmental impact assessment may be integrated into the existing procedures for consent to projects in the Member States, or, failing this, into other procedures or into procedures to be established to comply with the aims of this Directive.

3. Member States may, in exceptional cases, exempt a specific project in whole or in part from the provisions laid down in this Directive.

In this event, the Member States shall:

(a) consider whether another form of assessment would be appropriate and whether the information thus collected should be made available to the public;

(b) make available to the public concerned the information relating to the exemption and the reasons for granting it;

(c) inform the Commission, prior to granting consent, of the reasons justifying the exemption granted, and provide it with the information made available, where appropriate, to their own nationals.

The Commission shall immediately forward the documents received to the other Member States.

The Commission shall report annually to the Council on the application of this paragraph.

Article 3

The environmental impact assessment will identify, describe and assess in an appropriate manner, in the light of each individual case and in accordance with the Articles 4 to 11, the direct and indirect effects of a project on the following factors:

—human beings, fauna and flora,
—soil, water, air, climate and the landscape,
—the inter-action between the factors mentioned in the first and second indents,
—material assets and the cultural heritage.

Article 4

1. Subject to Article 2 (3), projects of the classes listed in Annex I shall be made subject to an assessment in accordance with Articles 5 to 10.

2. Projects of the classes listed in Annex II shall be made subject to an assessment, in accordance with Articles 5 to 10, where Member States consider that their characteristics so require.

To this end Member States may *inter alia* specify certain types of projects as being subject to an assessment or may establish the criteria and/or thresholds necessary to determine which of the projects of the classes listed in Annex II are to be subject to an assessment in accordance with Articles 5 to 10.

Article 5

1. In the case of projects which, pursuant to Article 4, must be subjected to an environmental impact assessment in accordance with Articles 5 to 10, Member States shall adopt the necessary measures to ensure that the developer supplies in an appropriate form the information specified in Annex III inasmuch as:

(a) The Member States consider that the information is relevant to a given stage of the consent procedure and to the specific characteristics of a particular project or type of project and of the environmental features likely to be affected;

(b) the Member States consider that a developer may reasonably be required to compile this information having regard *inter alia* to current knowledge and methods of assessment.

2. The information to be provided by the developer in accordance with paragraph 1 shall include at least:

—a description of the project comprising information on the site, design and size of the project,

—a description of the measures envisaged in order to avoid, reduce and, if possible, remedy significant adverse effects,

—the data required to identify and assess the main effects which the project is likely to have on the environment,

—a non-technical summary of the information mentioned in indents 1 to 3.

3. Where they consider it necessary, Member States shall ensure that any authorities with relevant information in their possession make this information available to the developer.

Article 6

1. Member States shall take the measures necessary to ensure that the authorities likely to be concerned by the project by reason of their specific environmental responsibilities are given an opportunity to express their opinion on the request for development consent. Member States shall designate the authorities to be consulted for this purpose in general terms or in each case when the request for consent is made. The information gathered pursuant to Article 5 shall be forwarded to these authorities. Detailed arrangements for consultation shall be laid down by the Member States.

2. Member States shall ensure that:

—any request for development consent and any information gathered pursuant to Article 5 are made available to the public,

—the public concerned is given the opportunity to express an opinion before the project is initiated.

3. The detailed arrangements for such information and consultation shall be determined by the Member States, which may in particular, depending on the particular characteristics of the projects or sites concerned:

—determine the public concerned,

—specify the places where the information can be consulted,

—specify the way in which the public may be informed, for example, by bill-posting within a certain radius, publication in local newspapers, organization of exhibitions with plans, drawings, tables, graphs, models,

—determine the manner in which the public is to be consulted, for example, by written submissions, by public enquiry,

— fix appropriate time limits for the various stages of the procedure in order to ensure that a decision is taken within a reasonable period.

Article 7

Where a Member State is aware that a project is likely to have significant effects on the environment in another Member State or where a Member State likely to be significantly affected so requests, the Member State in whose territory the project is intended to be carried out shall forward the information gathered pursuant to Article 5 to the other Member State at the same time as it makes it available to its own nationals. Such information shall serve as a basis for any consultations necessary in the framework of the bilateral relations between two Member States on a reciprocal and equivalent basis.

Article 8

Information gathered pursuant to Articles 5, 6 and 7 must be taken into consideration in the development consent procedure.

Article 9

When a decision has been taken, the competent authority or authorities shall inform the public concerned of:

— the content of the decision and any conditions attached thereto,

— the reasons and consideration on which the decision is based where the Member States' legislation so provides.

The detailed arrangements for such information shall be determined by the Member States.

If another Member State has been informed pursuant to Article 7, it will also be informed of the decision in question.

Article 10

The provisions of this Directive shall not affect the obligation on the competent authorities to respect the limitations imposed by nation regulations and administrative provisions and accepted legal practices with regard to industrial and commercial secrecy and the safeguarding of the public interest.

Where Article 7 applies, the transmission of information to another Member State and the reception of information by another Member State shall be subject to the limitations in force in the Member State in which the project is proposed.

Article 11

1. The Member States and the Commission shall exchange information on the experience gained in applying this Directive.

2. In particular, Member States shall inform the Commission of any criteria and/or thresholds adopted for the selection of the projects in question, in accordance with Article 4(2), or of the types of projects concerned which, pursuant to Article 4(2), are subject to assessment in accordance with Articles 5 to 10.

3. Five years after notification of this Directive, the Commission shall send the European Parliament and the Council a report on its application and effectiveness. The report shall be based on the aforementioned exchange of information.

4. On the basis of this exchange of information, the Commission shall submit to the Council additional proposals, should this be necessary, with a view to this Directive's being applied in a sufficiently coordinated manner.

Article 12

1. Member States shall take the measures necessary to comply with this Directive within three years of its notification([1]).

([1]) This Directive was notified to the Member States on 3 July 1985.

2. Member States shall communicate to the Commission the texts of the provisions of national law which they adopt in the field covered by this Directive.

Article 13

The provisions of this Directive shall not affect the right of Member States to lay down stricter rules regarding scope and procedure when assessing environmental effects.

Article 14

This Directive is addressed to the Member States.

Done at Luxembourg, 27 June 1985.

For the Council

The President

A. BIONDI

ANNEX I

PROJECTS SUBJECT TO ARTICLE 4 (1)

1. Crude-oil refineries (excluding undertakings manufacturing only lubricants from crude oil) and installations for the gasification and liquefaction of 500 tonnes or more of coal or bituminous shale per day.

2. Thermal power stations and other combustion installations with a heat output of 300 megawatts or more and nuclear power stations and other nuclear reactors (except research installations for the production and conversion of fissionable and fertile materials, whose maximum power does not exceed 1 kilowatt continuous thermal load).

3. Installations solely designed for the permanent storage or final disposal of radioactive waste.

4. Integrated works for the initial melting of cast-iron and steel.

5. Installations for the extraction of asbestos and for the processing and transformation of asbestos and products containing asbestos: for asbestos-cement products, with an annual production of more than 20 000 tonnes of finished products, for friction material, with an annual production of more than 50 tonnes of finished products, and for other uses of asbestos, utilization of more than 200 tonnes per year.

6. Integrated chemical installations.

7. Construction of motorways, express roads (1) and lines for long-distance railway traffic and of airports (2) with a basic runway length of 2 100 m or more.

8. Trading ports and also inland waterways and ports for inland-waterway traffic which permit the passage of vessels of over 1 350 tonnes.

9. Waste-disposal installations for the incineration, chemical treatment or landfill of toxic and dangerous wastes.

---

(1) For the purposes of the Directive, 'express road' means a road which complies with the definition in the European Agreement on main international traffic arteries of 15 November 1975.

(2) For the purposes of this Directive, 'airport' means airports which comply with the definition in the 1944 Chicago Convention setting up the International Civil Aviation Organization (Annex 14).

PROJECTS SUBJECT TO ARTICLE 4 (2)

1. Agriculture

   (a) Projects for the restructuring of rural land holdings.

   (b) Projects for the use of uncultivated land or semi-natural areas for intensive agricultural purposes.

   (c) Water-management projects for agriculture.

   (d) Initial afforestation where this may lead to adverse ecological changes and land reclamation for the purposes of conversion to another type of land use.

   (e) Poultry-rearing installations.

   (f) Pig-rearing installations.

   (g) Salmon breeding.

   (h) Reclamation of land from the sea.

2. Extractive industry

   (a) Extraction of peat.

   (b) Deep drillings with the exception of drillings for investigating the stability of the soil and in particular:

   — geothermal drilling,

   — drilling for the storage of nuclear waste material,

   — drilling for water supplies.

   (c) Extraction of minerals other than metalliferous and energy-producing minerals, such as marble, sand, gravel, shale, salt, phosphates and potash.

   (d) Extraction of coal and lignite by underground mining.

   (e) Extraction of coal and lignite by open-cast mining.

   (f) Extraction of petroleum.

   (g) Extraction of natural gas.

   (h) Extraction of ores.

   (i) Extraction of bituminous shale.

(j) Extraction of minerals other than metalliferous and energy-producing minerals by open-cast mining.

(k) Surface industrial installations for the extraction of coal, petroleum, natural gas and ores, as well as bituminous shale.

(l) Coke ovens (dry coal distillation).

(m) Installations for the manufacture of cement.

3. Energy industry

(a) Industrial installations for the production of electricity, steam and hot water (unless included in Annex I).

(b) Industrial installations for carrying gas, steam and hot water; transmission of electrical energy by overhead cables.

(c) Surface storage of natural gas.

(d) Underground storage of combustible gases.

(e) Surface storage of fossil fuels.

(f) Industrial briquetting of coal and lignite.

(g) Installations for the production or enrichment of nuclear fuels.

(h) Installations for the reprocessing of irradiated nuclear fuels.

(i) Installations for the collection and processing of radioactive waste (unless included in Annex I).

(j) Installations for hydroelectric energy production.

4. Processing of metals

(a) Iron and steelworks, including foundries, forges, drawing plants and rolling mills (unless included in Annex I).

(b) Installations for the production, including smelting, refining, drawing and rolling, of non-ferrous metals, excluding precious metals.

(c) Pressing, drawing and stamping of large castings.

(d) Surface treatment and coating of metals.

(e) Boilermaking, manufacture of reservoirs, tanks and other sheet-metal containers.

(f) Manufacture and assembly of motor vehicles and manufacture of motor-vehicle engines.

(g) Shipyards.

(h) Installations for the construction and repair of aircraft.

(i) Manufacture of railway equipment.

(j) Swaging by explosives.

(k) Installations for the roasting and sintering of metallic ores.

5. Manufacture of glass

6. Chemical industry

    (a) Treatment of intermediate products and production of chemicals (unless included in Annex I).

    (b) Production of pesticides and pharmaceutical products, paint and varnishes, elastomers and peroxides.

    (c) Storage facilities for petroleum, petrochemical and chemical products.

7. Food industry

    (a) Manufacture of vegetable and animal oils and fats.

    (b) Packing and canning of animal and vegetable products.

    (c) Manufacture of dairy products.

    (d) Brewing and malting.

    (e) Confectionery and syrup manufacture.

    (f) Installations for the slaughter of animals.

    (g) Industrial starch manufacturing installations.

    (h) Fish-meal and fish-oil factories.

    (i) Sugar factories.

8. Textile, leather, wood and paper industries

    (a) Wool scouring, degreasing and bleaching factories.

    (b) Maufacture of fibre board, particle board and plywood.

    (c) Manufacture of pulp, paper and board.

    (d) Fibre-dyeing factories.

    (e) Cellulose-processing and production installations.

    (f) Tannery and leather-dressing factories.

9. Rubber industry

Manufacture and treatment of elastomer-based products.

10. Infrastructure projects

  (a) Industrial-estate development projects.

  (b) Urban-development projects.

  (c) Ski-lifts and cable-cars.

  (d) Construction of roads, harbours, including fishing harbours, and airfields (projects not listed in Annex I).

  (e) Canalization and flood-relief works.

  (f) Dams and other installations designed to hold water or store it on a long-term basis.

  (g) Tramways, elevated and underground railways, suspended lines or similar lines of a particular type, used exclusively or mainly for passenger transport.

  (h) Oil and gas pipeline installations.

  (i) Installation of long-distance aqueducts.

  (j) Yacht marinas.

11. Other projects

  (a) Holiday villages, hotel complexes.

  (b) Permanent racing and test tracks for cars and motor cycles.

  (c) Installations for the disposal of industrial and domestic waste (unless included in Annex I).

  (d) Waste water treatment plants.

  (e) Sludge-deposition sites.

  (f) Storage of scrap iron.

  (g) Test benches for engines, turbines or reactors.

  (h) Manufacture of artificial mineral fibres.

  (i) Manufacture, packing, loading or placing in cartridges of gunpowder and explosives.

  (j) Knackers' yards.

12. Modifications to development projects included in Annex I and projects in Annex I undertaken exclusively or mainly for the development and testing of new methods or products and not used for more than one year.

ANNEX III

INFORMATION REFERRED TO IN ARTICLE 5 (1)

1. Description of the project, including in particular:

   — a description of the physical characteristics of the whole project and the land-use requirements during the construction and operational phases,

   — a description of the main characteristics of the production processes, for instance, nature and quantity of the materials used,

   — an estimate, by type and quantity, of expected residues and emissions (water, air and soil pollution, noise, vibration, light, heat, radiation, etc.) resulting from the operation of the proposed project.

2. Where appropriate, an outline of the main alternatives studied by the developer and an indication of the main reasons for his choice, taking into account the environmental effects.

3. A description of the aspects of the environment likely to be significantly affected by the proposed project, including, in particular, population, fauna, flora, soil, water, air, climatic factors, material assets, including the architectural and archaeological heritage, landscape and the inter-relationship between the above factors.

4. A description (¹) of the likely significant effects of the proposed project on the environment resulting from:

   — the existence of the project,

   — the use of natural resources,

   — the emission of pollutants, the creation of nuisances and the elimination of waste;

   and the description by the developer of the forecasting methods used to assess the effects on the environment.

5. A description of the measures envisaged to prevent, reduce and where possible offset any significant adverse effects on the environment.

6. A non-technical summary of the information provided under the above headings.

7. An indication of any difficulties (technical deficiencies or lack of know-how) encountered by the developer in compiling the required information.

(¹) This description should cover the direct effects and any indirect, secondary, cumulative, short, medium and long-term, permanent and temporary, positive and negative effects of the project.

1 Council Directive 85/337/EEC of 27 June 1985 on the assessment of the effects of certain public and private projects on the environment is printed in the Official Journal of the European Communities, page No. L 175/40 dated 5.7.85. It is reproduced at Appendix 7 to this booklet.

2 The following Regulations implementing the EC Directive have been made:

    i Town and Country Planning (Assessment of Environmental Effects) Regulations 1988 (SI No. 1199)

    ii Environmental Assessment (Scotland) Regulations 1988 (SI No. 1221)

    iii Environmental Assessment (Salmon Farming in Marine Waters) Regulations 1988 (SI No. 1218)

    iv Environmental Assessment (Afforestation) Regulations 1988 (SI No. 1207)

    v Land Drainage Improvement Works (Assessment of Environmental Effects) Regulations 1988 (SI No. 1217)

    vi Highways (Assessment of Environmental Effects) Regulations 1988 (SI No. 1241)

    vii Harbour Works (Assessment of Environmental Effects) Regulations 1988 (SI No. 1336)

    viii Town and Country Planning General Development (Amendment) Order 1988 (SI No. 1272). *Note*: revoked by SI 1988 No. 1813 (The Town and Country Planning General Development Order 1988). Provisions of SI 1988 No. 1272 now form Article 14(2) of the 1988 General Development Order.

    ix Town and Country Planning (General Development) (Scotland) Amendment Order 1988 (SI No. 977)

    x Town and Country Planning (General Development) (Scotland) Amendment No. 2 Order 1988 (SI No. 1249)

    xi Electricity and Pipe-line Works (Assessment of Environmental Effects) Regulations 1989 (SI No. 167). *Note*: revoked by SI 1990 No. 442 (see item xiv below).

    xii Harbour Works (Assessment of Environmental Effects) (No. 2) Regulations 1989 (SI No. 424)

    xiii Town and Country Planning (Assessment of Environmental Effects) (Amendment) Regulations 1990 (SI No. 367)

    xiv Electricity and Pipe-line Works (Assessment of Environmental Effects) Regulations 1990 (SI No. 442) xv Roads (Assessment of Environmental Effects) Regulations (Northern Ireland) 1988 (SR No. 344)

xvi Planning (Assessment of Environmental Effects) Regulations (Northern Ireland) 1989 (SR No. 20)

xvii Environmental Assessment (Afforestation) Regulations (Northern Ireland) 1989 (SR No. 226)

xviii Harbour Works (Assessment of Environmental Effects) Regulations (Northern Ireland) 1990 (SR No. 181)

3 The following Northern Ireland Regulations are in preparation:

i Environmental Assessment (Flood Relief Work) Regulations (Northern Ireland)

ii Environmental Assessment (Discharges to Water) Regulations (Northern Ireland)

4 *Guidance*

i DOE Circular 15/88 (Welsh Office Circular 23/88) "Environmental Assessment" dated 12 July 1988.

ii SDD Circular 13/88 "Environmental Assessment: Implementation of EC Directive: The Environmental Assessment (Scotland) Regulations 1988" dated 12 July 1988.

iii Forestry Commission booklet "Environmental Assessment of Afforestation Projects" dated 4 August 1988.

iv "Environmental Assessment of Marine Salmon Farms", note by Crown Estate Office dated 15 July 1988.

v DOE Circular 24/88 (Welsh Office Circular 48/88) "Environmental Assessment of Projects in Simplified Planning Zones and Enterprise Zones" dated 25 November 1988.

vi SDD Circular 26/88 "Environmental Assessment of Projects in Simplified Planning Zones and Enterprise Zones" (relates to Scotland) dated 25 November 1988.

vii DOE Memorandum on "Environmental Assessment" dated 30 March 1989 to the General Managers of New Towns Development Corporations and to the Chief Executive of the Commission for the New Towns (advice on projects arising in new towns).

viii DTp Departmental Standard notice HD 18/88 "Environmental Assessment under EC Directive 85/337" dated July 1989.

ix DOE free leaflet "Environmental Assessment".

x Welsh Office free leaflet "Environmental Assessment/Asesu'r Amgylchedd" (bilingual).

xi Scottish Office free leaflet "Environmental Assessment—a Guide".

Printed in the United Kingdom for HMSO.
Dd 0292742, C16, 9/90, GP 3385/2, CCN 16268.